Key Stage 2

# Non-fiction

Carol Matchett

Name _____

Schofield & Sims

# Introduction

Non-fiction writing is all around us, giving information and facts about the world. It isn't just found in books, for example, magazines, newspapers and many websites contain forms of non-fiction.

This book shows you how to read different types of non-fiction writing for information or interest. It explains the forms, purposes and features of non-fiction, with examples. The activities will help you develop your reading skills and your understanding of non-fiction texts. The book will also help you to improve your own non-fiction writing by thinking about the purpose and form of the writing and the audience you are writing for.

## Finding your way around this book

Before you start using this book, write your name in the name box on the first page.

Then decide how to begin. If you want an overview of the different sorts of non-fiction writing, which will help you to develop your skills at finding and using information, you should work right through the book from beginning to end. Another way to use the book is to dip into it when you want to find out about a particular topic, such as skim reading. The Contents page will help you to find the pages you need.

Whichever way you choose, don't try to do too much at once – it's better to work through the book in short bursts.

When you have found the topic you want to study, look out for these icons, which mark different parts of the text.

This icon shows you the activities that you should complete. You write your answers in the spaces provided. This book does not include answers to the activities because there are so many different possible answers and it wouldn't be practical to list all of them. Check your answers with an adult and when you are sure that you understand the topic, put a tick in the box beside it on the Contents page. On page 40 you will find suggestions for some projects (**Now you try**), which will give you even more opportunities to improve your understanding of reading and writing non-fiction.

**Explanation**

This text explains the topic and gives examples. Make sure you read it before you start the activities.

This text gives you useful background information about the subject.

# Contents

# Non-fiction books 1

## Explanation

Non-fiction books contain all sorts of fascinating **information** about people, places, objects, ideas and experiences. As well as giving information, they also **explain**, **explore** issues, give a glimpse into other people's lives and **tell us how** to do things.

## Activities

**1** People read **non-fiction** books for different reasons. Match the following titles to the **reader**.

**Baking for Beginners – 20 Simple Bakes**        someone researching recycling

**The Great Green Fact File**        someone who likes reading diaries

**Why is Blood Red? And Other Questions**        someone who collects recipes

**My Tour de France – a Day by Day Account**        someone who enjoys science

**2** Read the cover of this book. What do you think it could be about?

**Going for Gold**

Five Sporting Superstars

Five Fascinating Lives

**3** Read the cover of this book. Write **three** questions that the book might answer.

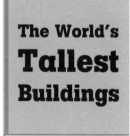

The World's **Tallest** Buildings

**4** Which of the **six** titles on this page would you most like to read? Give **reasons** for your choice.

The book I would choose is called _____

I would choose it because _____

_____

# Non-fiction books 2

## Explanation

Non-fiction books range from the textbooks you use at school to the information books in the library and the manuals (instruction books) you use at home. Inside these books you often find a **Contents page**, an **index** and **chapter** or **section headings**. These **features** help you find the information you want.

## Activities

**1** Choose the best word or phrase to complete each sentence of this passage about the **features** of a non-fiction book.

**a** You can find a list of all the page headings in the _____.

| cover | contents page | glossary | index |
|---|---|---|---|

**b** You could then skim read this (see page 8) to _____.

| find the pictures | find the meaning of a word | get an overview of the book |
|---|---|---|

**c** To find a page on a particular topic you could use the _____.

| index | glossary | blurb | references |
|---|---|---|---|

**d** This is at the back of the book and is organised in _____.

| time order | number order | alphabetical order | no particular order |
|---|---|---|---|

**2** Use the **Contents** on page 3 to find what is covered on different pages of this book. The first one has been done for you.

| Topic | Page | Topic | Page |
|---|---|---|---|
| Reference books | 6 | | 11 |
| Writing a newspaper report | | | 27 |
| Features of instructions | | | 29 |
| Now you try | | | 37 |

# Reference books

## Explanation

Reference books are a particular type of non-fiction. You use them to look up a particular **fact** or piece of **information** – not to read from cover to cover, just to dip in to. Reference texts are often organised in **alphabetical order** so it is easy to go straight to the page or entry needed.

## Activities

**1** You use **reference books** for different reasons. Match the books below to the **reason** for reading.

| | |
|---|---|
| **dictionary** | to find another word to use instead of 'fly' |
| **encyclopaedia** | to find the meaning or definition of a word |
| **thesaurus** | to find a map of Europe |
| **atlas** | to find the address of a local shop |
| **business directory** | to find out five facts about the planet Venus |

**2** Look at the list of reference books in activity 1.

**a** Which is *not* organised in alphabetical order? _____

**b** Which contains information on many subjects? _____

**3** **a** Here are some **facts** about lions written in note form. Add some more facts.

| fierce hunter | male is 1.2m tall | mane | plains of Africa & Asia |
|---|---|---|---|

_____

_____

**b** Continue this **entry** about lions for a children's animal encyclopaedia. It should sound **precise** and **factual**, as if it has been written by an expert.

**Lion** Lions are one of the largest members of the cat family. _____

_____

_____

_____

# Other non-fiction texts

## Explanation

Not all non-fiction writing comes in the form of a book. **Letters**, **leaflets**, **newspapers**, **magazines**, **brochures**, **adverts** or television **listings** are all examples of non-fiction texts that you might read every day.

The **internet** is another major source of information. You can access the internet in a variety of ways: from a PC or laptop to a tablet or mobile phone. Finding information on websites is different from finding information in a book.

## Activities

**1** Here are a few **opening words** taken from non-fiction texts. What sort of text do you think each one comes from?

**a** Dear Sir, I am writing to complain about … _____

**b** Tamworth pigs in great escape _____

**c** Visit Oakham Museum – open all year _____

**d** How to set up your new television _____

**2** Complete these flow charts to **compare** finding information in a **book** and **online**.

| Finding information in a book | Finding information online |
| --- | --- |
| Find a useful book by … | Find a useful website by … |
| ↓ | ↓ |
| Find the right page or section by … | Find the right webpage or section by … |
| ↓ | ↓ |
| Find (and record) the information you want by … | Find (and record) the information you want by … |

# Skim reading a report

You read non-fiction to learn more about a topic. Before you begin reading, quickly **skim** (glance over) a text to get an idea of what it is about.

## Activities

**1** **Skim read** this magazine article to get an overall understanding of the subject.

# Extreme sports

They began on city streets but are now among the fastest growing of all sports, with competitions held all around the world. Discover the thrills and spills of extreme sports.

### BMX – on your bike!

The original BMX (bicycle motocross) bikes, with a low seat and small wheels, were used for scrambling over rough ground. But soon riders realised they could use the bikes to perform tricks on the street, on the flat (known as *flatlanding*), on ramps or other obstacles, and over rocks and mudbanks.

**Essential equipment:** BMX bike, helmet, gloves, elbow and kneepads
**The basics:** wheelie, front-wheel balance, bunny hops or back hops
**Top tricks:** flair, double backflip, tailwhip, busdriver, grinds

### Inline skating – get your skates on!

Inline skating started in 1980 when an ice-hockey player set up the company Rollerblade®, making skates with wheels instead of blades. *Street skating* is popular in parks and some cycle routes but there are other inline activities: *speed skating*, *aggressive skating* (tricks and jumps using ramps), and sports such as *inline hockey*.

**Essential equipment:** multi-use skates, helmet, knee and elbow pads, wrist guards
**The basics:** ready position, A-frame, stroking and gliding, brake stop
**Top tricks:** grinds, toe-heel glide, back flips, frontside

### Skateboarding – all aboard!

The skateboard was invented when someone attached four wheels to a surfboard-shaped piece of wood. In the 1970s the kick tail was added and the base was spring-loaded to make it easier to perform tricks. There are now different styles of skateboarding: *street style*, *slalom* (fast around obstacles), *freestyle* (tricks on the flat), and *bowl* or *ramp riding*.

**Essential equipment:** skateboard, skate shoes with rubber soles, protective clothes
**The basics:** pushing, scooting, tail stall, kick turn
**Top tricks:** ollie, grabs, flip tricks, boardslides, 50–50 grinds

## Explanation

Non-fiction texts are organised and presented to help you find your way around the text. They usually are in different **sections** with **headings** and **subheadings** to show what each section is about. **Bold** or large print draws your attention to other important parts. **Skimming** (or **skim reading**) a text gives you an idea of the content and how the information is organised.

**2** Write down **four** things that you have learnt about the topic of the article on page 8 from your first **skim read**.

_____

_____

_____

_____

**3** **a** Skim the article again to see how it is organised. Place a letter in each empty box on page 8 to label the different parts. Use some of the letters more than once.

| **A** title | **B** introduction | **C** subheading | **D** description |

**b** What do the **subheadings** show you about how the information is organised?

_____

**4** Some parts of the article are in **bold** print. Why did the writer want to draw your attention to these parts?

_____

_____

**5** After skim reading the text, what do you understand about extreme sports? Write **two questions** that you would like the article to answer when you read it in more **detail**.

_____

_____

_____

# Gathering information

## Explanation

Sometimes you read non-fiction to find information, answer a question, or complete a task. If you know exactly what you want to find out, you can **scan** the text (quickly look over the page) looking for **key words**. This helps you find the part you need to read more carefully to answer your question. A **note-making table** is useful for recording the information you find.

## Activities

**1** Answer these questions by **scanning** the article on page 8 for **key words**.

   **a** What does **BMX** stand for? _____

   **b** What **sport** can **inline skaters** play? _____

   **c** How were **skateboards** improved in the **1970s**?

   _____

**2** Reread the article on page 8. Use this **note-making table** to **record information** about the three sports. Write **notes**, not complete sentences.

| | BMX | Inline skating | Skateboarding |
|---|---|---|---|
| **How the sport started** | | | |
| **Different types of activity** | | | |
| **Equipment** | | | |
| **First things to learn** | | | |

# Writing a report

**Activities**

**1** **a** Write an **article** for your school magazine about your favourite sport, style of music or hobby. Write your chosen topic in the box.

> My topic is

**b** Decide on some **subheadings** to help you organise and **group your ideas** and information into different **sections** or **paragraphs**. Then make **notes** about what you would include under each subheading.

| **Subheading** | **Subheading** |
|---|---|
|  |  |

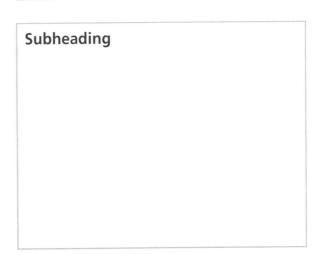

| **Subheading** | **Subheading** |
|---|---|
|  |  |

**c** Write your article on a separate piece of paper. Include an **introduction** and use the subheadings to tell the reader what each section is about. Use the article on page 8 as a model to help you write and present your article.

## Activities

**1** Here are some **instructions**. Read them carefully. Check they **make sense** and that you could follow them.

Try to **picture** each step or, if you have the materials available, try making the card.

# A secret greeting

Make your own greeting card for someone special – you can use this clever design for any occasion!

**You will need**

- an A4 piece of coloured card
- scissors
- a pencil
- 60cm of coloured ribbon
- glue
- wrapping paper, pictures from magazines or felt pens for decoration.

Diagram 1

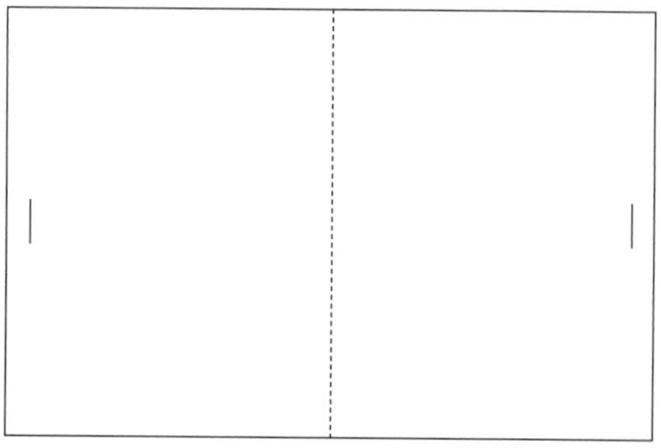

**What to do**

**1** Fold the piece of card in half and then open it out again.

**2** 1cm from the left-hand edge, draw a faint line 2cm long. Draw a similar line 1cm from the right-hand edge. (See Diagram 1.)

**3** Now cut along these two lines. Take care not to tear the edge of the card.

**4** Write your special secret message inside the card. Then fold it up again.

**5** Take the piece of ribbon and thread it through the two slits. Tie the ribbon in a neat bow.

**6** Now decorate the front of the card by drawing your own design or sticking on pictures cut from magazines or wrapping paper. (See Diagram 2.) Choose something that the person receiving the card will like.

Diagram 2

# Checking the details

**Explanation**

You read **instructions** to find out **how to do something**. It is important to read each **step** carefully and check that you understand what needs to be done. If you are not sure about a step, stop and reread it. There are often **details**, **tips** and **diagrams** to help you understand more difficult parts.

**2** What piece of equipment might be useful in **step 2** that is **not** listed under 'You will need'? Explain why it might be needed.

_____ . Because _____

_____ .

**3** How can you tell that **step 3** might be difficult to do?

_____

**4** In **step 4** it says 'write your special secret message'. Why is the message 'secret'?

_____

**5** Draw a diagram in the box to show what to do in **step 5**.

**6** The opening sentence says you can use the design 'for any occasion'. How might you adapt

step 6 to make a 'Get well soon' card? _____

_____

**7** **a** Tick one of the following. The instructions were

easy to follow ☐     a little difficult to follow ☐     very difficult to follow ☐

**b** Give a **reason** for your answer.

_____

_____

# Features of instructions

## Explanation

**Instructions** are usually easy to recognise because they have a number of familiar **features**. They are usually clearly presented with **lists**, **headings** and **subheadings** to make them easy to follow. There is usually a clear series of **steps**, often numbered, that explain what has to be done, in order.

## Activities

**1** Look at how the instructions on page 12 are **structured**. How do the **features** listed below help you to follow instructions?

**a**

> A list of items needed

_____

_____

**b**

> What to do, split into numbered steps

_____

_____

**c**

> A picture of the finished item

_____

_____

**2** Look at how the instructions are **presented**. Explain how these features help the reader.

**a** **Bullet points** in 'You will need' _____

**b** **Numbering** in 'What to do' _____

**c** The **diagram** for step 2 _____

_____

**3** There are many different sorts of instructions, such as recipes, directions, manuals and lists of rules. How would instructions in a computer manual be **similar** or **different** to the instructions on page 12?

**Similar** _____

**Different** _____

Non-fiction

# Improving and revising instructions

## Explanation

When you are writing instructions, think about your **purpose** and try to make them **clear** and **easy to follow**. Think about what your readers **need to know** and how you can **guide** them through the process. Instructions you have read (like those on page 12) will help you organise and present your instructions effectively.

## Activities

**1**  **a**  Here are some instructions that are not very easy to follow. Add steps or **more detail** to make the meaning clearer for the reader.

# How to play Snakes and Ladders

Throw the dice.

Move the counters along.

Go up the ladders and down the snakes.

The winner is the first one to get to the end.

**b**  Now read the new instructions as if you had never played the game. Do they **make sense**? Are they **precise**? Is everything **clear** and **easy to follow**? If not, then think about what changes you could make to improve them.

**2**  On a separate piece of paper, **rewrite** these instructions yourself, making sure they are as clear and easy to follow as you can make them. (Use the instructions on page 12 to help.)

**1** Read this **account** of the Great Plague to find out **what** happened, **where**, **when** and **why**. As you read, underline **dates**, **names** and **key events**.

# Bring out your dead!

In summer 1665, chilling cries of 'Bring out your dead!' echoed through the empty streets of London. This was the year of the Great Plague, when over 100 000 people died from this terrible disease.

In March 1665, people had seen a comet in the sky. As they did not know about comets, they thought it was a sign that God was angry and something terrible was going to happen. The very next month it did.

On 12 April, in one of the poorest areas of London, Margaret Ponteous was buried. She was the first known victim of the Great Plague, which then spread quickly through other areas. The disease is now thought to have been carried by rats that lived on rubbish thrown into the narrow, overcrowded streets.

By mid-June the Plague had spread throughout the city. A thousand people died from it each week. Samuel Pepys wrote in his diary: 'I did in Drury-lane see two or three houses marked with a red cross upon the doors and "Lord have mercy upon us" writ there'. The red cross showed that someone in that house had the Plague. All Londoners dreaded seeing this sign.

On 27 July the King, Charles II, left London. By this time over 200 000 people had already fled to escape the horror of the Plague. The people who remained in London felt deserted.

By August, 7000 people were dying each week. The Lord Mayor of London, Sir John Lawrence, issued further orders to deal with the Plague and ordered all public places to be shut. But in September the number of cases rose again. Corpses littered the streets and huge pits were dug to bury them.

Only in December did the number of people dying start to fall. Finally, the worst was over and in February 1666 it was safe for King Charles to return to London.

## Did you know?

Samuel Pepys kept a diary from January 1660 until May 1669. He wrote about the Great Plague of 1665 and the Great Fire of 1666, as well as personal things, like his home and his wife.

# How accounts are organised

## Explanation

An **account** describes an event – it tells us what happened. **Factual accounts**, like the one on page 16, are often found in history books. They usually describe events in **time order**, like a story. **Text marking** (such as underlining dates, places and the main event in each paragraph) will help you to keep track of **what** happened, **where** and **when**.

The **main events** in an account can be recorded on a **flow chart** or **timeline**.

**2** Use your **text marking** on page 16 to make a **timeline** showing the **main events** described.

— March 1665 – comet seen over London.

— 12 April 1665 –

# Scanning for information

## Explanation

Sometimes you need to go back and **check details** about events. **Scanning** for **dates**, **names** or **key words** will help you quickly find the part you need to read in detail. To **understand** people's actions or why events happened, you often need to **read carefully**, thinking about **key details** and working out (or **inferring**) reasons, thoughts and feelings.

## Activities

**1** **Scan** the text on page 16 to find these names. Explain **who** these people were and **why** they were significant at the time.

a Margaret Ponteous _____.

b Charles II _____.

c Sir John Lawrence _____.

**2** Answer these questions about the events. Use page 16 to help.

a Why did Londoners dread seeing the sign of the **red cross**?

_____

b Why did the Lord Mayor order all public places to be shut in **August**?

_____

c Why were the streets of London empty in **summer 1665**? Give **two** or **three** reasons.

_____

_____

_____

**3** What do you think Londoners were thinking and feeling at these times?

a The comet appears. _____.

b The king leaves. _____.

c The king returns. _____.

Non-fiction

# Writing an account

## Explanation

When writing non-fiction it is important to choose a **style** that fits the **purpose**, **form** and **audience** for your writing. For example, if you are recounting an amusing event in a **letter** to your best friend, you would use a chatty, **informal style**, but if you are writing a **factual account** to impress your teacher, a more **formal style** is needed.

## Activities

**1** Here is a rather boring **account** of an adventure weekend. Imagine you are writing to a **friend**. Use an **appropriate style** and add details and comments to make the account **lively** and **appealing** to your reader. You can make up the details but try to make it sound real!

Recently I went on an adventure weekend. _____

_____

On the Saturday morning we went riding. _____

_____

In the afternoon we went to the beach and tried bodyboarding.

_____

_____

On the Sunday morning we went on a bike trail. _____

_____

In the afternoon we had lessons in kayak canoeing. _____

_____

We all agreed it was a great weekend.

**2** Now, on a separate piece of paper, **rewrite** the account for the **school governors**, who organised the weekend. Use a more **formal style** and change the details and comments to fit the new audience.

# Comparing accounts 1

## Explanation

As well as factual accounts there are also **personal accounts**, where writers describe something that happened to them, based on their personal **experience** of an event. Personal accounts are found in **diaries**, **journals**, **letters** and **autobiographies**. They include feelings and **comments** on the events.

## Activities

**1**  **a**  Read these extracts from the diary of Samuel Pepys. Underline examples of **personal experiences** or **comments**.

> **April 30th 1665** Great fears of the Sicknesses here in the City, it being said that two or three houses are already shut up. God preserve us all.
>
> **June 7th 1665** This day, much against my Will, I did in Drury-lane see two or three houses marked with a red cross upon the doors, and 'Lord Have Mercy upon Us' writ there …
>
> **July 17th 1665** … people here are afeared of London, being doubtful of anything that comes from thence or that hath lately been there … I was forced to say that I lived wholly at Woolwich.
>
> **August 28th 1665** But now, how few people I see, and those walking like people that have taken leave of the world …

**b**  How does this **personal account** add to your understanding of the events described on page 16?

_____

_____

**c**  Which parts best show the **feelings** of people at the time?

_____

**2**  Complete this table by **comparing** the **account** on page 16 with the **diary** above.

|  | Bring out your dead! | Pepys' diary |
|---|---|---|
| **Who wrote it** | unnamed writer | Samuel Pepys |
| **When** | in 21st century |  |
| **Form** | a factual, historical account |  |
| **Purpose** (for whom/why) |  |  |
| **Language** |  |  |

# Comparing accounts 2

## Explanation

Biographies and autobiographies are **accounts of a person's life**. An **autobiography** is written in the **first person** *by* the actual subject (the person it is about). A diary is one example of autobiographical writing. A **biography** is written in the **third person** about the subject.

## Activities

**1  a**  Read this information about Samuel Pepys.

> Samuel Pepys is probably the greatest English diary writer of all time. He began his diary in January 1660 and wrote it until 31 May 1669. He was an important man and the diary gives us a very good picture of life in London at that time. He lived through both the Great Plague of 1665 and the Great Fire of 1666, and wrote about both events in vivid detail. Pepys wrote his diary in a sort of shorthand and it was not until 1825 that his words were translated and the diary was published.

**b**  How can you tell this is from a **biography**, not an autobiography?

_____

**c**  Read the passage again. Underline any **comments** made about Samuel Pepys.

**2**  The following sentences have been taken from **different types of text**. Draw lines to match each **sentence** to the **text** it comes from.

| | |
|---|---|
| **August 1665** To the Exchange, where I have not been a great while. | a medical dictionary |
| Samuel Pepys was born in 1633. | a biography of Samuel Pepys |
| The plague was first brought to Europe by rats aboard ships sailing from other countries. | the diary of Samuel Pepys |
| **Plague**: infectious disease usually transferred from rats to humans by infected fleas or from person to person. | a history book about diseases and medicine |

**1** Read this newspaper **headline**. Think what the story might be about.

# Sighting sets off wild boar hunt

**A family picnicking on Ashview Hill last weekend were left in a state of shock after a close encounter with a dangerous wild boar.**

The Desai family had just sat down to enjoy their picnic when they heard a loud grunting. They turned around and were horrified to see a hairy beast about the size of a small pony emerge from undergrowth just metres away.

Hari Desai shows our reporter the site of the family picnic.

Local rangers searched the area but so far this is the only reported sighting. The rangers say they cannot be certain that it was a wild boar. They continue to search for tracks, markings on trees or other signs that could prove there are wild boars living in the parkland.

Large numbers of wild boar are known to have lived in the area 500 years ago, when it was mainly forest. But their numbers fell and eventually they died out over 300 years ago. In recent years, some boars may have escaped from farms or wildlife parks and started living in the wild. However, the sighting at the weekend was the first in this area.

The Desai family are convinced they saw a wild boar. Hari Desai, aged 10, told our reporter, 'It was bigger than a pig and very hairy. It may have had tusks but I didn't want to get too close.'

Visitors are warned not to approach the animal if it is sighted. A parkland warden said that although boars would not normally attack humans, a mother defending its young could be dangerous.

# Features of a newspaper report

**2** Read the **first sentence** of the report on page 22. Answer these questions.

   **a**   **What** happened? _____

   **b**   **Where** did it happen? _____

   **c**   **When** did it happen? _____

   **d**   **Who** was involved? _____

**3** Write **two questions** that you hope the rest of the report will answer.

_____

_____

**4** Read the rest of the report and write down the **main points** that are made in each paragraph.

| |
|---|
| Paragraph 1   It was only metres away from them. |
| Paragraph 2 |
| Paragraph 3 |
| Paragraph 4 |
| Paragraph 5 |

**5** What **other questions** about the event come into your mind?

_____

# Comparing and inferring viewpoints

## Explanation

Everyone has their **own view** of an event. That is why news reports often include **comments** or **quotes** about the events from the **different people** who were involved. Sometimes you can **infer** (or work out) a person's view from their role in the event.

## Activities

Use what you have read on page 22 to help you consider these **different viewpoints**.

**1** The reporter spoke to **Hari's mother** about the events. Write what you think she said to the reporter.

**Reporter:** Mrs Desai, how did you feel when you saw the wild boar?

**Mrs Desai:** _____

_____

_____

**2** **Hari** wrote about the events in his **diary**. What do you think he wrote?

**Saturday** _____

_____

_____

_____

**3** One of the **parkland rangers** wrote an **official report** on what happened. What do you think she wrote?

At 1.25 pm we received an emergency call from a mobile phone _____

_____

_____

_____

# Writing a newspaper report

## Explanation

When writing a **news report**, think of yourself as a news **reporter**. Think about news reports you have read or heard and use these as models for your own writing. Picture the **structure** of a news report with a **headline**, an **opening sentence** and a series of **short paragraphs** that develop the story. As you write, copy the **style** and **voice** of a news report so your writing sounds convincing.

## Activities

**1** Here are some **notes** made by a local news reporter. Use them to write an interesting and convincing **news report**. Add **details** and **comments** of your own.

> Theft from local museum – valuable Roman statue missing
> Tuesday (while open to public) – no witnesses
> Theft discovered by Brian Samuels (museum guide). Glass case empty.
> No clues. Alarm failed. Police baffled.

**Headline**

_____

_____

_____

_____

_____

_____          _____

_____          _____

## Activities

**1** Read these four advertisements.

**A**

# Feel the **Splash!** sensation

# splash!

The new sports drink with a delicious fruity fizzzzz

**more than a drink — a sense-ation**

Comes in five exciting new flavours as refreshing as a shower of tropical rain

**B**

# Phone Fun

**The funkiest phones, the coolest colours and the latest dazzling designs**

Don't be shown up by your mates – upgrade your mobile **NOW**!

For the best choice in mobile phones and for a full colour catalogue, just contact us at **Phone Fun**

**C**

## NOAH ANIMAL HOSPITAL

*Five million wild birds and animals are injured each year in the UK alone. Many of these injuries are caused by people.*

Here at the **Noah Animal Hospital** we treat these animals completely free of charge. Where possible, we release them back into the wild when they are fit and well.

We deal with 10 000 calls a year.

No creature is ever turned away.

**Help us to help defenceless animals**
*'A truly great cause!'*

**D**

# Luxury holiday homes in the sun

* a brand new development of villas and apartments

* beautiful views, overlooking the sea

* every villa has its own pool

Don't miss this great opportunity to buy

# your place in the sun

# Fact and opinion

**Advertisements** are an example of **persuasive writing**. Persuasive writing **tries to convince** us to believe it. It is important to **recognise** persuasive writing and be aware of the **writer's motives** and **purpose**. Read critically; think about the claims made. Are they facts or opinions? **Facts** are definitely true and can be proved; **opinions** are what *some* people might say but are not definitely true – they cannot be proved.

Adverts make **appealing claims**, but there might be some **things they don't tell us**.

**2** Read advertisement **A** on page 26. Tick the box to show whether each of these statements is a **fact** or an **opinion**.

| | Fact | Opinion |
|---|---|---|
| Splash! is a new fizzy drink | ☐ | ☐ |
| Splash! is delicious | ☐ | ☐ |
| Splash! is refreshing | ☐ | ☐ |
| Splash! comes in five flavours | ☐ | ☐ |

**3** Read advertisement **C**. Write down **two facts** about Noah Animal Hospital and **one opinion**.

**Fact** _____

**Fact** _____

**Opinion** _____

**4** **a** Read advertisement **B**. Write down **two appealing claims** made about Phone Fun.

_____

_____

**b** Read advertisement **D**. Write down **two** things that the advertiser might **not** have told us.

_____

_____

**Did you know?**

The first printed advertisements appeared in the weekly newspapers produced during the seventeenth century. Before the time of newspapers, advertising was done by street criers who went round the streets calling people's attention to items for sale.

# Features of advertisements

## Activities

**1**   **a**   **Reread** the adverts on page 26 and underline words and phrases used for a **persuasive effect**.

     **b**   Tick a box below for the advert that you found most persuasive.

       ☐ **A**     ☐ **B**     ☐ **C**     ☐ **D**

     **c**   Give **two reasons** why you found it persuasive.

_____

_____

**2**   Answer these questions about the **language** used in the adverts.

     **a**   In advertisement **A** it says that Splash! is '**as refreshing as a shower of tropical rain**'. Why is it described in this way?

_____

     **b**   Advertisement **B** (Phone Fun) is aimed at **young people**. Find and copy **two or three phrases** that show this.

_____

_____

     **c**   In advertisement **C** it says 'Help us to help defenceless animals'. Why has the word '**defenceless**' been used?

_____

**3**   Look at the **presentation** in advertisement **D**. Why has the large **picture** been used?

_____

_____

# Writing an advertisement

## Explanation

When you are trying to persuade someone, think about how you will interest and convince your audience. Think about the **impact** and effect of your language choices. **Appeal** to your reader, using use **positive** and **persuasive language**. Don't be afraid to **exaggerate** (for example, say something is *fantastic, incredible, mind-blowing, out of this world*).

## Activities

**1** Write an **advertisement** for a new crispy snack. The advert should appeal to someone of **your age**. Think what would capture your interest and persuade you.

   **a** **Note** some ideas and **persuasive words** and **phrases**.

| Convincing or appealing claims | Words and phrases to persuade |
|---|---|
| | |

   **b** Choose what **form** of advertisement you will write. Tick one.

full-page advertisement for magazine ☐      flyer to hand out in shop ☐

script for radio advert ☐      script for television advert ☐

   **c** Think about how you would use **pictures**, **sounds** or **presentation** to add to the effectiveness of your advert. Note your ideas here.

**2** Now write or design your advertisement on a separate piece of paper. Write as if you are **speaking** to your reader. Choose language, style and presentation to **appeal** to your audience.

## Activities

**1** Read this **discussion** about sport in schools. Think about the issue.

# Should there be more sport in school?

This is a question that affects **you**, so what do **you** think? There are important points to be made by both sides.

## FOR more sport

People want to see UK athletes win gold medals. We all want our national teams to be successful. However, top coaches say that sport is not taken seriously enough in UK schools. In the USA, one of the most successful sporting nations, PE and games are on the school timetable three or four times a week – in this country it can be less than two hours.

It is not just at the top level that sport is important. Experts claim that basic coordination skills, important in all areas of life, must be developed early. With less time spent on sport, these skills will not be developed.

Moreover, many argue that sport teaches social skills, such working in a team, and how to win and lose. How will children learn these skills if they don't play sport?

Even more importantly, sport helps us to stay healthy. A recent survey found that half the children surveyed were not doing the daily hour of exercise needed to keep fit. Surely, schools should be doing *more* to encourage children to take part in sport – not *less*.

## AGAINST more sport

There are only so many hours in a school day. If more time is spent on sport, then music, art or drama might be cut instead. Is that fair?

Many would argue that most of the school day should be spent on reading, writing and mathematics. These are the subjects children are tested in and parents want their children to do well at. Children can do sports in their spare time, but there are fewer opportunities for learning to read and write out of school.

Indeed, many primary schools do not have the facilities to teach some sports properly. For example, a tarmac playground is not the best place to learn cricket. Often children are better off joining a club.

As for staying fit and healthy … isn't that more to do with reducing the amount of time spent sitting at home in front of the TV? Children in America do lots of sport at school, but the country still has the highest obesity levels in the world.

Now you have heard both sides of the argument. What do **you** think?

# Summarising the main ideas

**2**  **a**  Reread the discussion on page 30 about sport in schools. Underline or highlight the **main points** made **for** and **against** it.

 **b**  After the introduction, how is the text **organised**?

_____

_____


**3**  In the table below, write a **summary** of the main points for and against more sport.

| For more sport | Against more sport |
|---|---|
| • | • |
| • | • |
| • | • |
| • | • |


**4**  Read the statements below and tick which one you think is true.

 **a**  The writer thinks that there should be more sport in school.  ☐

 **b**  The writer thinks that there is no need for more sport in school.  ☐

 **c**  The writer leaves it up to the reader to decide.  ☐

# Features of a discussion

A **debate** is a **formal discussion** of an issue, where people say what they think. When taking part in a discussion or debate it is important to give **reasons** and **evidence** to support the points you make. The evidence might be an example of a particular case, a fact or a statistic, or sometimes a statement from an expert or a trusted source.

## Activities

**1** Imagine you are taking part in a **debate** on the issue of sports in school. Having read the discussion on page 30, **which side** would you be on? What is **your view**?

I think _____

because _____

_____

**2** Decide on **two points** to make in the debate to support your view. Use details or quotations from page 30 as **evidence** to help support these points.

**Point 1**

Evidence: _____

_____

_____

**Point 2**

Evidence: _____

_____

_____

**3** Reread the **arguments** on page 30 and find a point you **do not** agree with. Explain **why** you disagree.

I don't agree that _____

because _____

_____

# Writing a discussion

Explanation

To **compare** two views in writing, you first need to gather together ideas from **both sides**. Use knowledge from other subjects, your own real-life experiences, and **evidence** from reading and research. **Note** the ideas in lists to help you to **organise** and **plan** your writing. You will need enough ideas and detail to sound convincing.

## Activities

**1** Imagine that your school is deciding whether to spend money on a new **library** or new **sports facilities**. You are asked to write an **article** for the school magazine setting out **both sides** of the **argument**. **Plan** below what you would write.

Title _____

Introduce the issue _____

| Points for a new library | Points for new sports facilities |
|---|---|
| • | • |
| • | • |
| • | • |
| • | • |
| • | • |
| • | • |
| Evidence I need | Evidence I need |

Conclusion _____

_____

**2** Make sure you have a number of points for each side. Then write the article on a separate piece of paper. Use adverbials to **develop and contrast points**, such as 'For example', 'Indeed', 'However', 'On the other hand', 'In contrast'.

# Reading an explanation

## Activities

**1** Read this **explanation** of earthquakes. Read carefully, checking it **makes sense**. Underline anything you are not sure about.

### Earthquakes

Beneath the surface, the Earth is made up of huge, flat pieces of rock called **plates**. At a **fault line** (the place where two plates meet) the plates can move and rub against each other, or slide under each other. These movements cause vibrations or tremors that reach the Earth's surface.

Directly above, at the **epicentre**, the ground can be crunched up or torn apart. The movements force **seismic waves** across the Earth's surface. These waves move outwards just like the ripples on a pool when you throw in a pebble. They cause the ground to vibrate and shake, which can set off landslides and damage buildings and other structures.

As buildings are shaken by earthquake tremors, the stress and movements cause walls to crack and foundations to move. Some buildings may collapse. Smaller quakes, or **aftershocks**, that follow the main quake often cause further damage to already weakened buildings.

Countries such as Japan that have a lot of earthquakes build low buildings or earthquake-proof structures. Engineers design buildings that bend and sway with the movement instead of cracking.

If an earthquake occurs under an ocean it can cause a huge wave of water called a **tsunami**. These waves travel quickly across the ocean, growing in size and power as they approach a shoreline. When a tsunami reaches the coast it crashes into the land, engulfing anything in its way.

| | |
|---|---|
| **epicentre** | the point on the Earth's surface directly above the source of the quake |
| **seismic wave** | the energy created by an earthquake |

## Explanation

**Explanations**, such as those you read in science or geography, help you understand **how** and **why** things happen. They may be difficult to understand. They often describe a series of linked events and it is important to check you understand as you read. If you get confused or don't understand, **stop**, **reread**, **think**. Try to imagine what is described, using pictures or **diagrams** to help. Try explaining it **in your own words**.

**2** Explain **in your own words** what causes an earthquake.

_____

_____

**3** Complete this **flow chart** to show the **sequence of events** described in paragraph 2 of 'Earthquakes'.

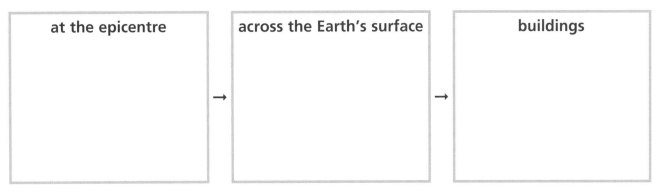

| at the epicentre | | across the Earth's surface | | buildings |

**4** **a** Explain **why buildings collapse** in earthquakes.

_____

_____

**b** Buildings in Japan are made '**earthquake proof**'. Explain what this means and why it is important.

_____

**5** Explain what happens when an earthquake occurs **under an ocean**.

_____

_____

**6** How does the **diagram** help you understand the information given in the **last paragraph**?

_____

# Technical words

## Explanation

Explanations often include a lot of **technical words** related to the subject. It is important to understand the meaning of these words. Fortunately, writers usually explain them – for example, by giving a **definition** in brackets or in a **glossary**.

## Activities

**1** Some words on page 34 stand out because they are in **bold** print. Why are they written like this?

_____

**2** In the **first paragraph**, why has the writer used **brackets**?

_____

**3** After the **last paragraph**, some words are listed in a **text box**. What is the purpose of this?

_____

_____

**4** The writer says seismic waves move '**like the ripples on a pool**' – why does the writer use this **simile**?

_____

**5** Here are some **technical words** used on page 34. Find each one in the text and then write a **definition** to explain its meaning.

**a** aftershock _____

**b** epicentre _____

**c** fault line _____

**d** plates _____

**e** tsunami _____

Non-fiction

# Writing an explanation

## Explanation

Explaining things means **giving reasons**. When you are writing an explanation use words that link ideas and show how one thing causes or results in another.

**Example** because     so     if     then     causes     results in

Remember, you should also try to sound like an **expert**, so use the correct **technical words**.

## Activities

**1** **a** Write a **leaflet** for children **explaining** why it is important to brush your teeth. It should answer this child's questions.

> Why should I brush my teeth?

> Why do I need toothpaste?

> What will happen if I don't?

**b** **Draft** what you will write using the **diagram** below to help you.

**Why brushing your teeth is important**

_____

_____

_____

_____

cavity —        plaque    _____

_____

gum —    _____

_____

**2** Read your draft to make sure everything is **clearly explained**. Then decide how to **present** the information in the form of a leaflet. Use a separate piece of paper to do this.

## Explanation

After reading, you sometimes need to **present information** in a **different form**. This means thinking about what you have read, deciding what is relevant and choosing how to organise the information in the new form. A **planning frame** can help you **organise** and **develop your ideas** before you write.

For the following tasks you need to **reuse information** from other pages in this book. It may help to reread the relevant pages.

## Activities

**1**  The account of the Plague on page 16 is too long to fit into a history book for children. Write a **one-paragraph summary** of the main points using no more than **100 words**.

    **a**  **Plan** your account by making a **list** of the **points** to include.

- 
- 
- 
- 
- 

    **b**  Write the summary on a separate piece of paper. As you write, try **combining** two or three points into one sentence to keep the summary **concise**.

**2**  **a**  Write a **comparison** of an earthquake and a tsunami for a **children's website**, referring to page 34 for ideas. Use the table below to help you think about their **similarities** and **differences**.

|  | Earthquake | Tsunami |
|---|---|---|
| How it is caused |  |  |
| What happens |  |  |
| Dangers, damage |  |  |

    **b**  Write your comparison on a separate piece of paper. Use words and phrases like these to help you make comparisons: 'both', 'however', 'while', 'whereas' in 'contrast'.

**3** You have been testing the new drink Splash! shown on page 26. The makers now want you to write an **evaluation** of the product.

    **a** Plan by thinking and making **notes** about **good points** and **things to improve**.

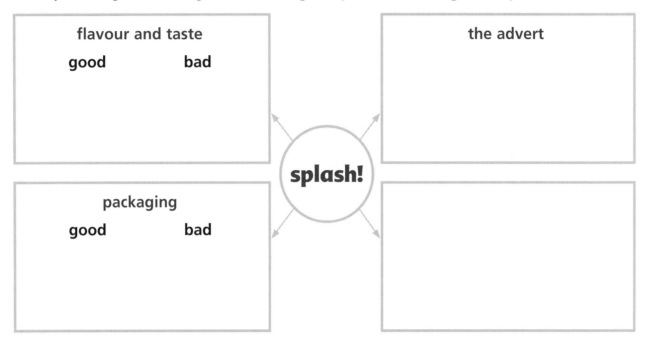

| flavour and taste |
| good          bad |

| the advert |

**splash!**

| packaging |
| good          bad |

    **b** Write your evaluation on a separate piece of paper. Use adverbials to help comment or contrast ideas, such as 'However', 'On the other hand', 'Unfortunately'.

**4**   **a** The warden featured in the news report on page 22 wants a **short**, **factual description** of a wild boar to help visitors identify the animal. Note details to include.

| Size | Behaviour |
|------|-----------|
|      |           |
| Features | Where seen |
|      |           |

    **b** Write your description on a separate piece of paper. Be **informative** and **precise**, like an **expert**.

---

When **writing non-fiction** texts, remember to:

- think **why** you are writing, **what** you are writing and **who** you are writing for
- use a planning frame to **organise** your ideas
- use similar texts you have read to help you **organise**, **write** and **present** your text
- sound knowledgeable and confident – like a non-fiction writer.

## Read all about it

Start reading the headlines in newspapers and see if you can guess what the story is about. Choose a story that sounds interesting and read it. Does it tell you everything you want to know? Does it stick to facts or does it include opinions?

## The persuaders

Adverts are everywhere – in newspapers, magazines, on television and on posters. Remember adverts try to persuade you to buy what they are selling. Choose one advertisement to read in more detail. How much of the advertisement is fact, how much opinion and how much exaggeration? Do you believe all the claims?

## Non-fiction challenge

You might often read non-fiction books on subjects that interest you, but occasionally try choosing a book on a subject you don't know much about. It may be a more of a challenge but you are sure to discover a whole new fascinating subject.

## Dear diary

Start writing a diary – you never know, perhaps one day you will be famous and it could be published! Record things that happen to you, with lots of interesting details and personal comments.

## Instructions, instructions

You will find lots of instructions around your house. Look in magazines, on food packages and in leaflets that come with new appliances. Read the instructions and see how easy or difficult they are to follow. Give them marks out of ten. Could you improve them?

## Cuttings file

Start to collect examples of different forms of non-fiction writing: letters, leaflets, adverts, and cuttings of newspaper reports or magazine articles. Keep them in a folder so that when you are asked to write something, you will have some good examples to use as models.